STAR WARS®

CLONE WARS
ADVENTURES
VOLUME 8

designers
Darin Fabrick and Josh Elliott

assistant editor
Dave Marshall

editor
Jeremy Barlow

publisher
Mike Richardson

special thanks to Elaine Mederer, Jann Moorhead,
David Anderman, Leland Chee, Sue Rostoni, and
Amy Gary at Lucas Licensing

The events in these stories take place sometime
during the Clone Wars.

www.titanbooks.com

www.starwars.com

STAR WARS: CLONE WARS ADVENTURES Volume 8, October 2007.
Published by Titan Books, a division of Titan Publishing Group Ltd., 144 Southwark
Street, London SE1 0UP. Star Wars ©2007 Lucasfilm Ltd. & ™. All rights reserved.
Used under authorization. Text and illustrations for Star Wars are © 2007 Lucasfilm
Ltd. No portion of this publication may be reproduced or transmitted, in any form or
by any means, without the express written permission of the copyright holder. Names,
characters, places, and incidents featured in this publication either are the product of
the author's imagination or are used fictitiously. Any resemblance to actual persons
(living or dead), events, institutions, or locales, without satiric intent, is coincidental.
PRINTED IN ITALY

2 4 6 8 10 9 7 5 3 1

STAR WARS®

CLONE WARS
ADVENTURES
VOLUME 8

"VERSUS"
script and art **The Fillbach Brothers**
colors **Tony Avina**

"OLD SCORES"
script **Chris Avellone**
art **The Fillbach Brothers**
colors **Pamela Rambo**

"ONE OF A KIND"
script **Jason Hall**
art **Ethen Beavers**
colors **Ronda Pattison**

"PATHWAYS"
script **Jeremy Barlow**
art **The Fillbach Brothers**
colors **Dan Jackson**

lettering
Michael Heisler

cover
The Fillbach Brothers and Dan Jackson

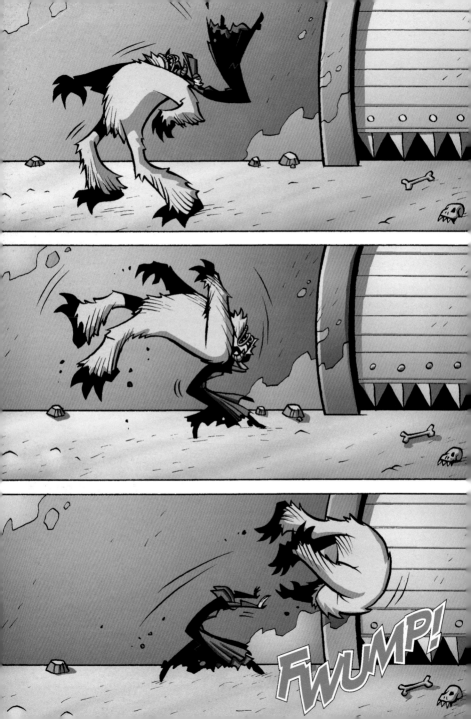

FWUMP!

SMACK!!

‹YOU CHEATED! JEDI MAGIC!›

NO, MONDO-MOD. I USED SIMPLE PHYSICS. THE WAMPA'S SIZE WAS ITS DOWNFALL.

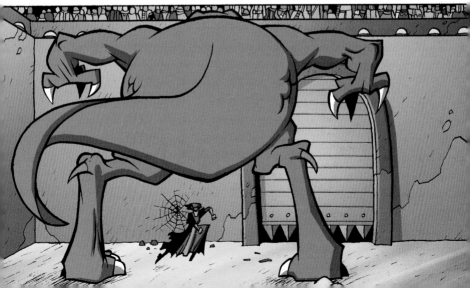

fwip!

BWOOM!

YES, MONDO-MOD... SIMPLE PHYSICS.

THE BIGGER AND STUPIDER THEY COME, THE HARDER THEY FALL.

HUMPF!

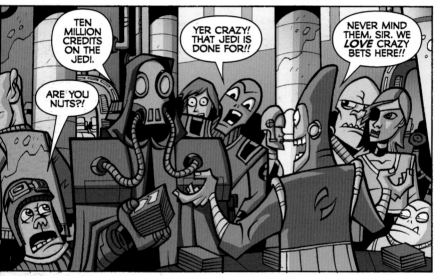

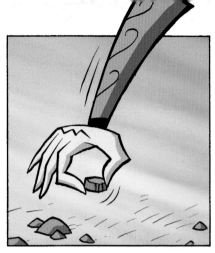

PAP!

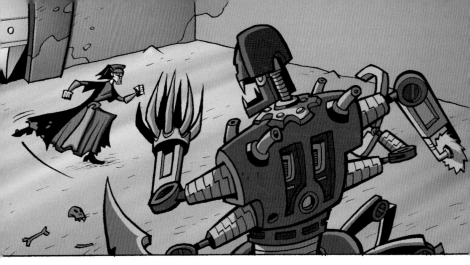

FWOOOSH!

KISH!

...AND MONDO-MOD DON'T NEVER WANNA SEE YOU AGAIN!

WORRY NOT. HE WON'T.

I HOPE YOU GOT WHAT YOU FOUGHT SO HARD FOR.

YES. THE HUTT WASN'T LYING. WE NOW HAVE THE COORDINATES TO A SECRET SEPARATIST WEAPONS FACTORY ON DIORDA.

AND HOW DID THE BETTING GO FOR YOU, BARRISS?

tshh!

WELL, LET'S JUST SAY THAT MONDO-MOD'S *"ARENA OF DOOM"* WILL BE CLOSED DUE TO LACK OF FUNDS...

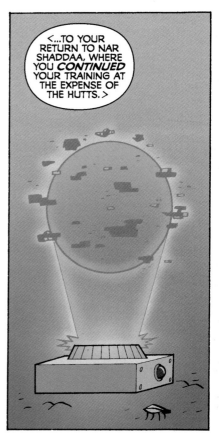

<...YOU WERE NOT THE **ONLY** ONE TO ANSWER MY CONTRACT.>

<YOU WILL NOT LEAVE THE SMUGGLER'S MOON ALIVE.>

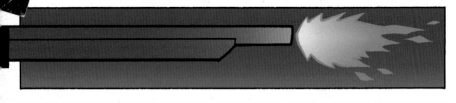

KA-BOOM!!

AMATEURS.

NEED SOME DISTANCE.

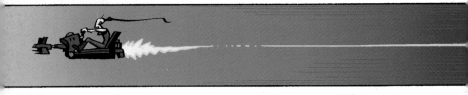

THE BOUNTY HUNTER, *JANGO FETT.*

MORE SPECIFICALLY, HIS *GENETIC MATERIAL.*

THE MAN *HIMSELF* WAS SLAIN ON *GEONOSIS.*

BUT WE'VE LEARNED *THE SEPARATISTS* ARE PLANNING TO THROW A HYDROSPANNER INTO THE WORKS --

-- BY STEALING HIS *GENE SAMPLE* AND CUTTING OFF OUR SUPPLY OF CLONES AT *THE SOURCE.*

INCOMING MESSAGE FROM CORUSCANT--

VIANNA!

YOU SEEM *UPSET,* JEDI...

Zeltrons (con't): They naturally project powerful pheromones, as well as possess empathic abilities that allow them to sense the emotions of other sentient beings. *-- Plevitz Essential Guide to Species*

WELL, YOU CAN ALWAYS MAKE MORE...

SNAP!

OH, WAIT....I GUESS *NOT.*

I'M *NOT* LETTING YOU LEAVE WITH THAT.

Zeltrons: While Zeltrons have little concern for military defense, they tend to keep themselves in peak physical condition.

FWOOSH!!

IT'S BEEN FUN, JEDI -- BUT I HAVE A *DELIVERY* TO MAKE.

Zeltrons (con't): When a Zeltron is deprived of the opportunity to love, he or she may resort to violence. In turn, they are known to be excellent warriors when possessing no other outlet for their passion.
-- *Plevitz Essential Guide to Species*

THE
END

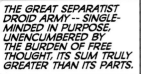

THE GREAT SEPARATIST DROID ARMY -- SINGLE-MINDED IN PURPOSE, UNENCUMBERED BY THE BURDEN OF FREE THOUGHT, ITS SUM TRULY GREATER THAN ITS PARTS.

MANY A WORLD HAS BEEN PUT UNDER ITS METALLIC BOOT-TREAD.

WHILE HOVERTANKS AND SPIDER DROIDS STRIKE TERROR IN THE ENEMY'S HEART, NEITHER WOULD SUCCEED WITHOUT THE **BATTLE DROID** -- THE SKELETAL AUTOMATONS THAT FORM THE LEGION'S BACKBONE.

A CLANKETY-CLANKING SWARM CONNECTED THROUGH THE CONTROL CORE'S HIVE-MIND, THEIRS IS THE GREATER POWER --

-- THE STRENGTH OF **NUMBERS**.

INTERCHANGEABLE AND ESSENTIALLY DISPOSABLE, THEIR UBIQUITY RENDERS THE INDIVIDUAL DROID PRACTICALLY **INVISIBLE**.

PLUS OR MINUS, ONE DROID HARDLY MAKES A DIFFERENCE.

TAKE ONE OUT AND TWO MORE ROLL OFF THE LINE TO REPLACE IT.

IF THERE WERE AWARENESS, THERE MIGHT BE COMFORT IN THAT ANONYMITY.

TEK!

BUT HOW COULD THEY KNOW...?

ITS LIFE FLASHES PAST ITS PHOTORECEPTORS --

-- MARCHED INTO BATTLE TIME AND AGAIN --

-- ONLY TO BE DESTROYED, SALVAGED, REBUILT, AND REDEPLOYED --

-- A LIFE OF RECYCLED HORROR.

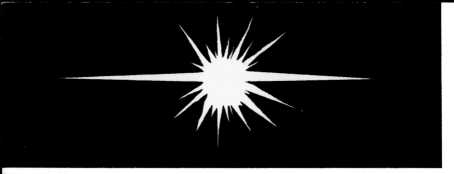

AND YET...AND YET EVEN MORE FRIGHTENING IS THE STRANGE NEW WORLD TO WHICH HE AWAKENS.

HIS CONNECTION TO THE COLLECTIVE SEVERED, THE VOICE OF THE HIVE-MIND SILENCED...

...FOR THE FIRST TIME HIS REASON OF BEING IS IN QUESTION...

...AND THROUGH THE CHAOS, A *NEW* DIRECTIVE TAKES HOLD--

-- SELF-PRESERVATION AT ALL COSTS!

PUTTING SEVERAL KILOMETERS BETWEEN HIMSELF AND HARM'S WAY, HE WRESTLES WITH HIS NEW COGNIZANCE.

HIS FUTURE UNCERTAIN, HE KNOWS ONE THING --

-- HE'S NOT ABOUT TO GRIND THIS NEW LIFE AWAY IN THE GEARS OF WAR.

ONE LAST CHANCE TO GO BACK. ONE MORE STEP TO THE POINT OF NO RETURN.

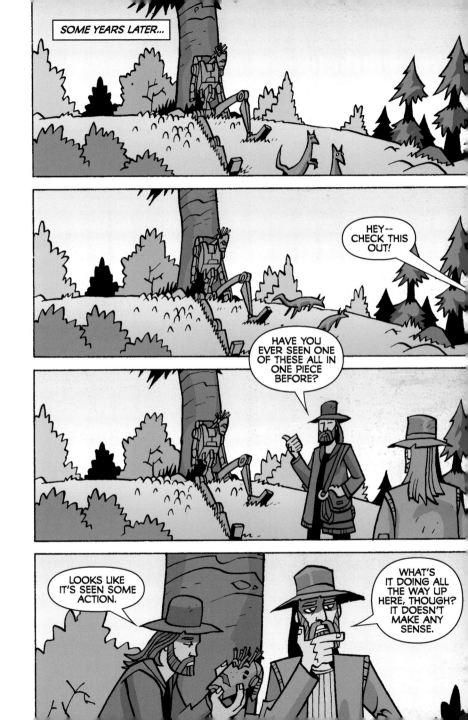

LEGO STAR WARS

CONTROL THE ACTION... AND DECIDE THE FATE OF THE GALAXY!!